KEEP CALM AND PLAY ON

CW00420360

WISE PUBLICATIONS
part of The Music Sales Group

London / New York / Paris / Sydney / Copenhagen / Berlin / Madrid / Hong Ko

30127075658075

Published by
WISE PUBLICATIONS
14-15 Berners Street, London W1T 3LJ,
United Kingdom.

Exclusive Distributors:
MUSIC SALES LIMITED
Distribution Centre, Newmarket Road,
Bury St Edmunds, Suffolk IP33 3YB,
United Kingdom.

MUSIC SALES PTY LIMITED
Units 3-4, 17 Willfox Street, Condell Park, NSW 2200,
Australia.

Order No. AM1006280
ISBN 978-1-78038-998-1
This book © Copyright 2013 Wise Publications,
a division of Music Sales Limited.

Edited by Jenni Norey.
Printed in the EU.

YOUR GUARANTEE OF QUALITY
As publishers, we strive to produce every book to
the highest commercial standards.
This book has been carefully designed to minimise awkward page turns
and to make playing from it a real pleasure.
Particular care has been given to specifying acid-free, neutral-sized
paper made from pulps which have not been elemental chlorine bleached.
This pulp is from farmed sustainable forests and was
produced with special regard for the environment.
Throughout, the printing and binding have been planned to ensure a sturdy,
attractive publication which should give years of enjoyment.
If your copy fails to meet our high standards, please inform us
and we will gladly replace it.

www.musicsales.com

ANGEL

Words & Music by Sarah McLachlan.

wreck-age___ of your si - lent___ rev-er - ie.___ You're in the arms of___ the

an - gel;___ may you find___ some_ com - fort___ here.___

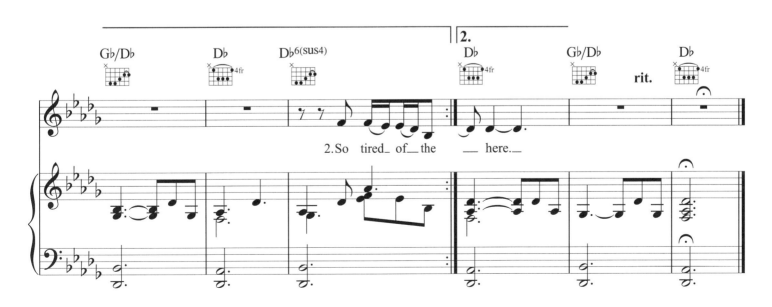

2.So tired_ of_the ___ here.___

BACK TO BLACK

Words & Music by Amy Winehouse & Mark Ronson.

BORN TO TRY

Words & Music by Delta Goodrem & Audius Mtawarira.

1. Do - ing ev-'ry-thing___ that I___ be lieve___ in going by the rules___ that I've been taught.___

More un-der-stand-ing of what's___ a-round___ me___

Con pedale

DREAM CATCH ME

Words & Music by Crispin Hunt, Newton Faulkner & Gordon Mills.

HEART ON MY SLEEVE

Words & Music by James Morrison & John M Shanks.

HURT

Words & Music by Linda Perry, Christina Aguilera & Mark Ronson.

1. Seems like it was yes - ter - day_ when I saw your face.

(2.) _ in - side,_ but I won't ad - mit_ it.

thank you for all you've done,_____ for - give all your___ mis - takes._____ There's
look - ing down___ up - on_____ me? Are you proud of who___ I am?_____ There's

noth - ing I would - n't do_____ to hear your voice_____ a - gain.____ Some -
noth - ing I would - n't do_____ to have just one_____ more chance,___ to

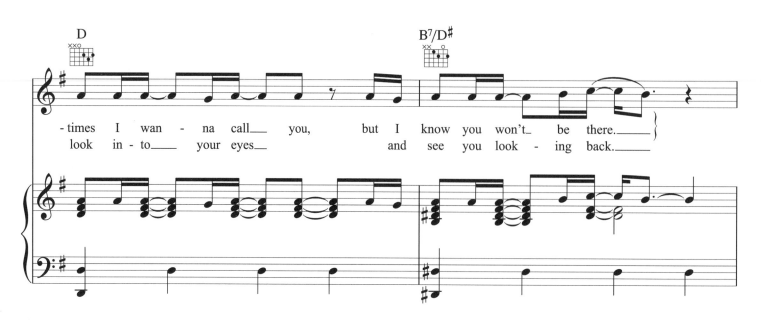

- times I wan - na call____ you, but I know you won't___ be there._____
look in - to____ your eyes____ and see you look - ing back.____

Whoa,_____ I'm sor - ry for_____ blam - ing_____ you_____

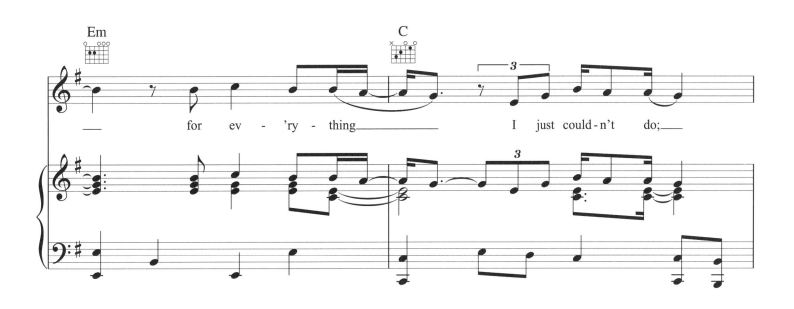

_____ for ev - 'ry - thing_____ I just could - n't do;_____

and I've hurt_____ my - self_____ by hurt - ing

you.   2. Some days I feel broke —self,_____   oh._____

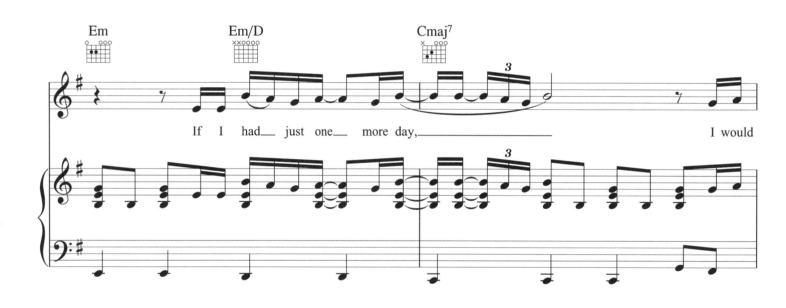

If I had_ just one_ more day,_____   I would

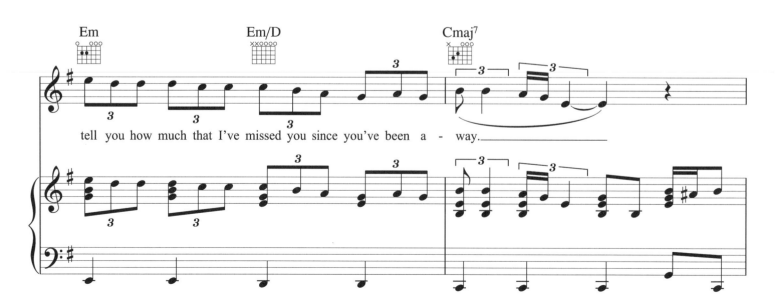

tell you how much that I've missed you since you've been a - way._____

IF THIS ISN'T LOVE

Words & Music by Brian Seals, Theron Thomas & Timothy Thomas.

JEALOUSY

Words & Music by Will Young, James Eliot & Jemima Stilwell.

THE MAN WHO CAN'T BE MOVED

Words & Music by Andrew Frampton, Steve Kipner,
Mark Sheehan & Daniel O'Donoghue.

1. Go - ing back to the cor - ner where I first saw you. Gon -

-na camp in my sleep - ing bag.__ I'm not gon-na move. Got some words on card - board, got

MAKE YOU FEEL MY LOVE

Words & Music by Bob Dylan.

1. When the rain is blow-ing in your face, and the whole world is on

2. When the eve-ning shad-ows and the stars ap-pear, and there is no - one there to dry

to make you feel my love.

A MOMENT LIKE THIS

Words & Music by Jorgen Elofsson & John Reid.

Well, I____ may be dream - ing, but still lie a - wake.___

Can't we make_ this dream_ last_ for ev - er?___ And I'll

cher - ish all__ the love____ we share.___ A mo - ment like this._

__ Some peo - ple wait_ a life - time for a mo - ment like this.__

MORE THAN THIS

Words & Music by Jamie Scott.

1. I'm broken, do you hear me?
2. I'm danc-ing a lone.

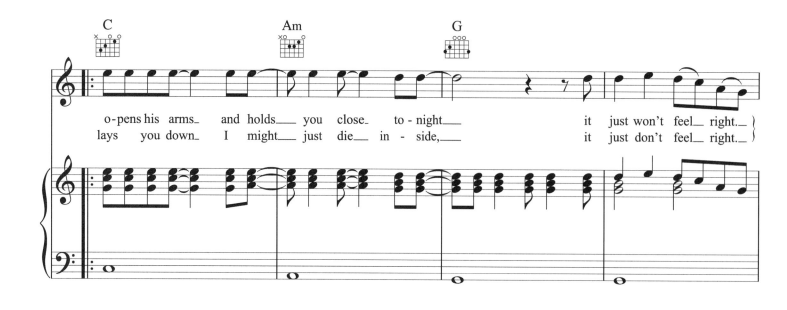

o-pens his arms and holds you close to-night it just won't feel right.
lays you down I might just die in - side, it just don't feel right.

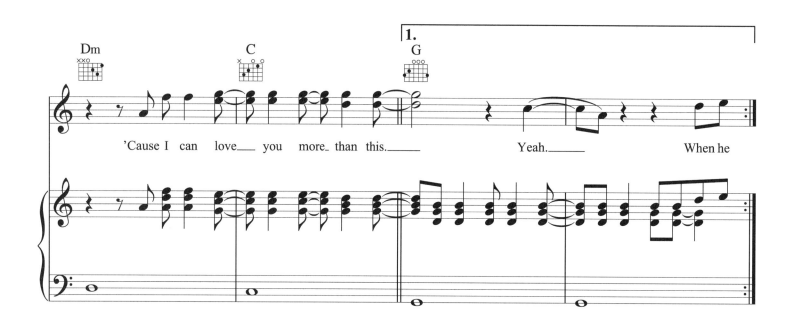

1.

'Cause I can love you more than this. Yeah. When he

2.

Can love you more than this.

PROUD

Words & Music by Lorne Tennant, Mich Hansen, Daniel Davidsen, Oritsé Williams, Marvin Humes, Jonathan Gill, Aston Merrygold & Jason Gill.

1. When my strength was gone and I just gave up on life, in my darkest place you were my guide.

2. I never gave up then 'cause you said keep hope alive. And a champion gives one last try, yeah.

PLEASE, PLEASE, PLEASE, LET ME GET WHAT I WANT

Words & Music by Morrissey & Johnny Marr.

So for once in my____ life____ let me____ get what I____ want.____ Lord knows it would be the first time.____ Lord knows

it would be the first time.___

So

So, for once in my _____ life let me _____ get what I _____ want.

Lord knows it would be the first time.

NEXT TO ME

Words & Music by Harry Craze, Hugo Chegwin,
Emeli Sande & Anuk Paul.

1. You won't find___ him drink - ing un - der ta - bles,
2. You won't find___ him try'n'___ to change___ the dev - il

roll - ing___ dice and stay - ing out___ till three.
for mon - ey, fame,___ for pow - er, out___ of greed.

SAIL AWAY

Words & Music by David Gray.

Sail a-way with me, hon-ey, I put my heart in your hand.

Sail a-way with me hon-ey now,_____ now,_____ now._____

Verse 2:
I've been talking drunken gibberish,
Falling in and out of bars.
Trying to get some explanation here
For the way some people are.
How did it ever come so far?

Chorus 5:
Sail away with me, honey
I put my heart in your hands.
It breaks me up if you put me down, whoa.
Sail away with me; what will be will be.
I wanna hold you now, now, now.

Chorus 6 & 7:
(Whistle)

SHE WILL BE LOVED

Words & Music by Adam Levine, James Valentine,
Jesse Carmichael, Mickey Madden & Ryan Dusick.

D.S. al Coda

THE SILENCE

Words & Music by Nadir Khayat, Savan Kotecha & Bilal Hajji.

SKINNY LOVE

Words & Music by Justin Vernon.

my my my,__ my my my__ my my.___   Star - ing at the

sink   of   blood   and crushed ven - eer.___

2. Tell my love__ to wreck__ it all.

Cut out all__ the ropes_ and let__ me__ fall.___   My__ my my,_

THE SOUND OF SILENCE

Words & Music by Paul Simon.

flash of a ne-on light_____ that split the night and touched the
voi-ces__ nev-er share_____ and no one dare dis-turb the

sound of si-lence._____
sound of si-lence._____
"Fools!" said I,"You do not know

si-lence like a can-cer grows."
"Hear my words that I might teach you,__

take my arms that I might reach you"— but my words like

si - lent rain-drops fell, and

ech - oed_____ in the wells of si - lence._____

5. And the peo - ple bowed and prayed to the ne - on god they

RUN

**Words & Music by Gary Lightbody, Jonathan Quinn,
Mark McClelland, Nathan Connolly & Iain Archer.**

WARWICK AVENUE

Words & Music by James Hogarth, Aimee Duffy & Francis Eg White.

1. When I ___ get to War-wick Av-e-nue ___ meet ___ me
(2.) get to War-wick Av-e-nue ___ we'll spend an

by the en-trance of ___ the tube. We can ___ talk things o-ver ___ a lit-tle
hour but no more than ___ two. Our on-ly chance to speak once

time.___ Prom - ise me___ you won't step___ out___ of line.___
more.___ I showed you the an-swers, now___ here's___ the door.___

When I___ get to War-wick Av-e-nue___ please_ drop_
When I___ get to War-wick Av-e-nue___ I'll tell you

the past and be___ true. Don't think we're_ O. K. just__ be-cause I'm_

WE ARE YOUNG

Words & Music by Jeff Bhasker, Nate Ruess,
Andrew Dost & Jack Antonoff.

WHO KNEW

Words & Music by Alecia Moore, Lukasz Gottwald & Max Martin.

1. You took my hand, you showed me how. You promised me you'd be around. Uh-huh. That's right.

2. Remember when we were such fools and so convinced and just too cool. Oh, no. No, no.

YOU GOT THE LOVE

Words & Music by Anthony Stephens, John Bellamy,
Arnecia Harris & John Truelove.

Some-times it seems__ the go-ing is just too rough. And things go wrong no mat-ter what__ __ I do.__ Now and then__ it seems that__ life is just too__ much.__ But you've got the love__ I need to see me through. When food is gone__ you are__ my dail - y meal.__ Oh.__ When friends__ are gone__ I know my

YOU RAISE ME UP

Words & Music by Brendan Graham & Rolf Løvland.

YOUR LOVE IS KING

Words & Music by Sade Adu & Stuart Matthewman.

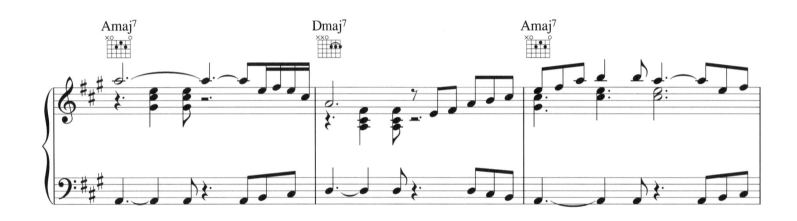

Your love is

king,_____ crown you with my heart,_ your love is king,_____ { (1, 3.)
(2.) you're the

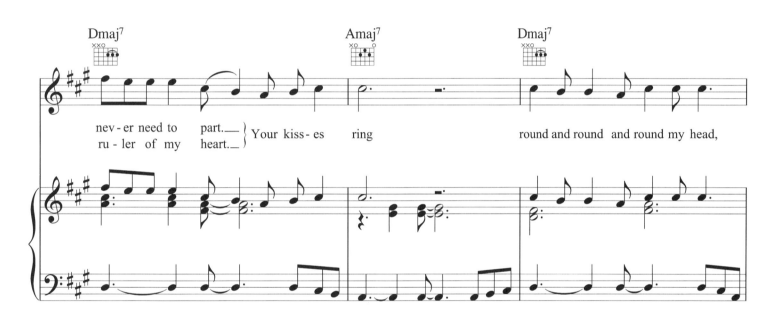

nev - er need to   part.__ } Your kiss- es   ring   round and round and round my head,
ru - ler of my   heart.__

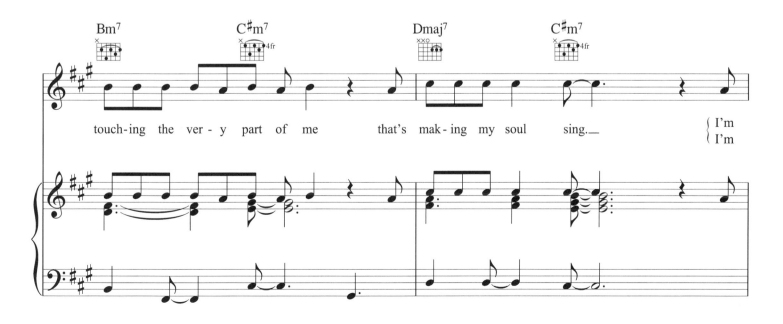

touch-ing the ver - y part of me   that's mak- ing my soul   sing.__   { I'm
I'm

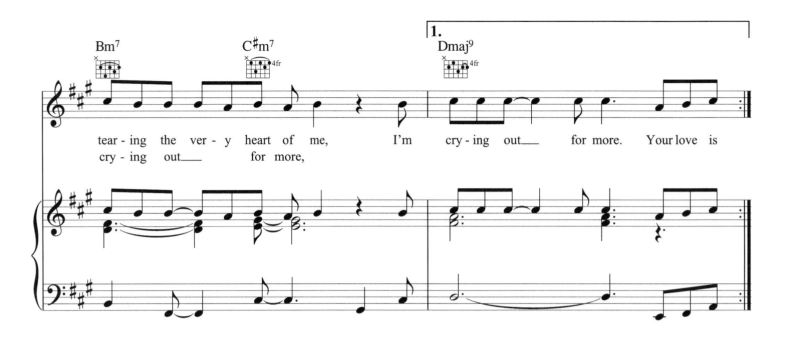

tear - ing the ver - y heart of me, I'm cry - ing out___ for more. Your love is
cry - ing out___ for more,

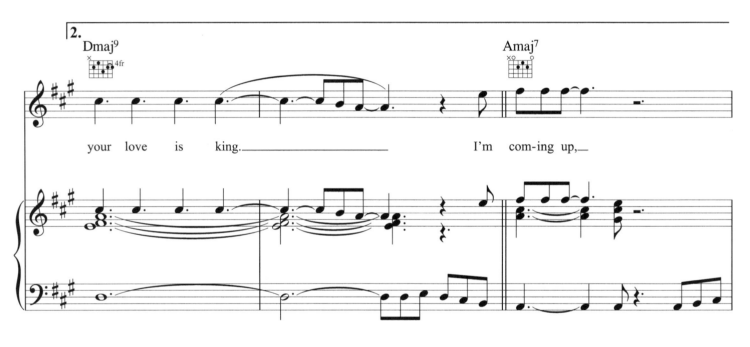

your love is king._____ I'm com - ing up,___

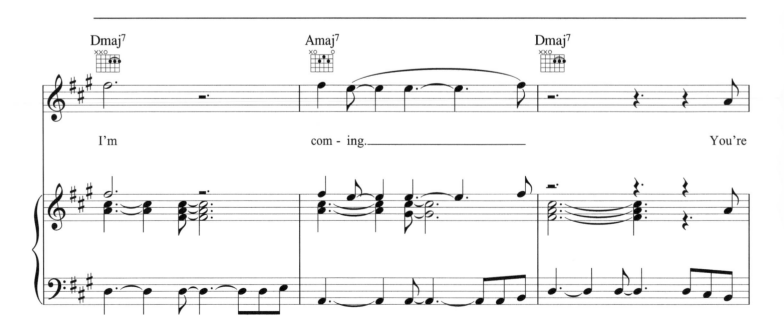

I'm com - ing._____ You're

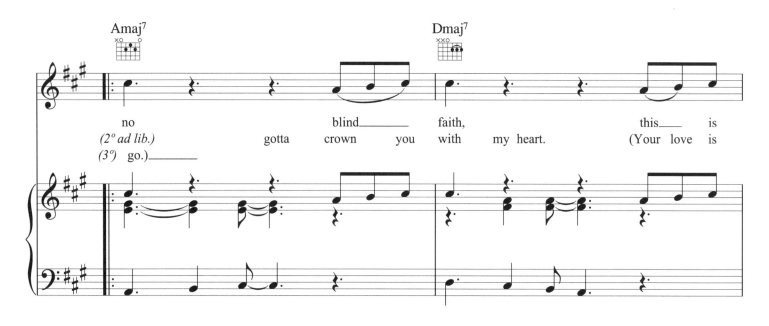

KEEP CALM
AND
PLAY SOME
MORE

available from all good
music shops

or, in case of difficulty, contact the Marketing Department.
Music Sales Limited, Newmarket Road, Bury St Edmunds, Suffolk, IP33 3YB, UK
marketing@musicsales.co.uk